# The Roger Hudson
# Guitar Method
# for
# Classical and Fingerstyle Guitarists

ROGER HUDSON MUSIC

## www.rogerhudson.com

# From the Author

As of the 2018 date of this publication, I have been teaching guitar for approximately 40 years! I have used many method books for my classical and fingerstyle guitar students. For my students also interested in other styles, I have used either no written "method" at all or a multitude of sources. Often my instructions in a lesson were - and sometimes still are – hand-written or typeset for a specific student and application. Nonetheless, when pertinent, I have generally preferred to use some sort of guitar method. A good method book can give the student and teacher a practical reference for organizing lessons and charting improvement. While writing my book, I have considered the best that I remember from the method books I have used in the past. This book builds on traditional fundamentals while presenting a modern menu of musical genres.

Now that we are well into the 21st century, I have re-assessed what I think a method book should be. Information (good and bad) is so readily available to teachers and students via digital media that I believe a practical method book need not be overly filled with detailed technical specifics. Sometimes controversial, concerns such as sitting position, nail shape (or no nail at all), rest stroke/free stroke, etc. have been intentionally omitted. These details can be immediately accessed now electronically, but sources should be vetted with the assistance of a qualified instructor. This book allows plenty of space for instructors' personal opinions regarding technical concerns and preferences. Guitar playing is, after all, an art. There will be subjectivity. Hopefully this book frees the instructor from having to serve as an editor. However, I do include a few tips which I deem to be of practical or fundamental necessity. Also, as a supplement to this book, I will be producing videos on concepts that are best demonstrated rather than merely explained.

This book is filled mostly with playing material – that is, music I have composed and sourced for students (and teachers) to enjoy. For aspiring classical guitarists – who are expected to read notes – and fingerstyle guitarists with a desire to complete their musical literacy, this book features only standard notation (except for the TAB fingerboard chart on page 4).

The *Roger Hudson Guitar Method* is indeed a method book in the sense that it moves systematically from simpler to more complex concepts. Once again, it is best used in tandem with a qualified teacher or mentor. This qualified person can give details on hand positioning, tone production and other physical concerns. Your teacher can also assist you in learning the vast landscape of musical terminology. I have concentrated my efforts in this book on progressive musical development while offering an interesting variety of music.

I hope this book enriches your musical life!

Roger Hudson
December 2018

# Contents

# Complete Notes of the Guitar
*20 fret fingerboard*

The TAB staff shows all possible locations for each note

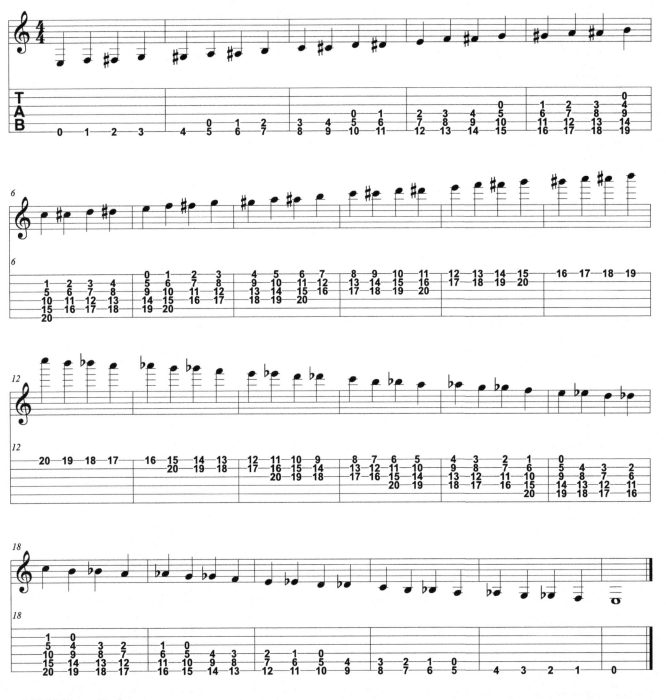

# Common Note Values

| | Note Symbol | | Rest Symbol |
|---|---|---|---|
| **Whole note = 4 beats duration** | 𝅝 | | ▬ |
| Dotted half note = 3 beats duration | 𝅗𝅥. | | ▬. |
| **Half note = 2 beats duration** | 𝅗𝅥 | | ▬ |
| Dotted quarter note = 1½ beats duration | ♩. | | 𝄽. |
| **Quarter note = 1 beat duration** | ♩ | | 𝄽 |
| Dotted eighth note = ¾ beat duration | ♪. | | 𝄾. |
| **Eighth note = ½ beat duration** | ♪ single | beamed group | 𝄾 |
| **Sixteenth note = ¼ beat duration** | ♬ single | beamed group | 𝄿 |

# Rhythm Training

*Tap even beats with your foot while clapping the rhythm patterns.*

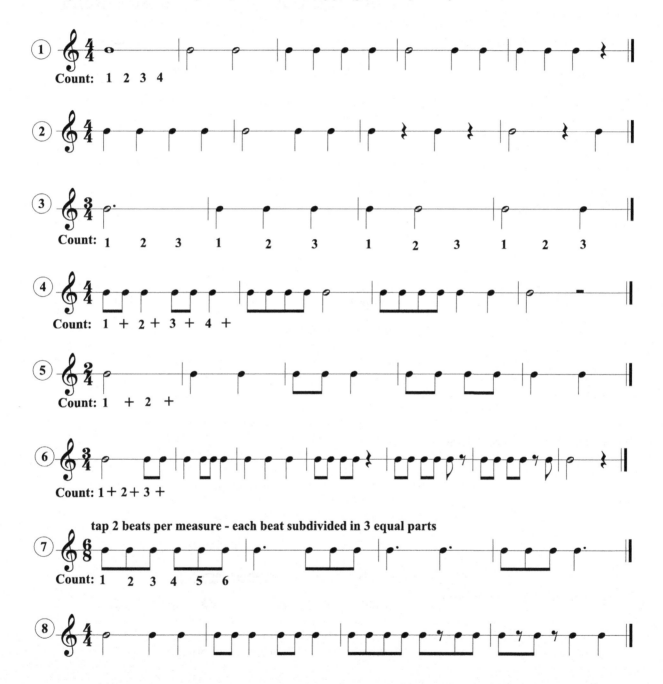

**tap 2 beats per measure - each beat subdivided in 3 equal parts**

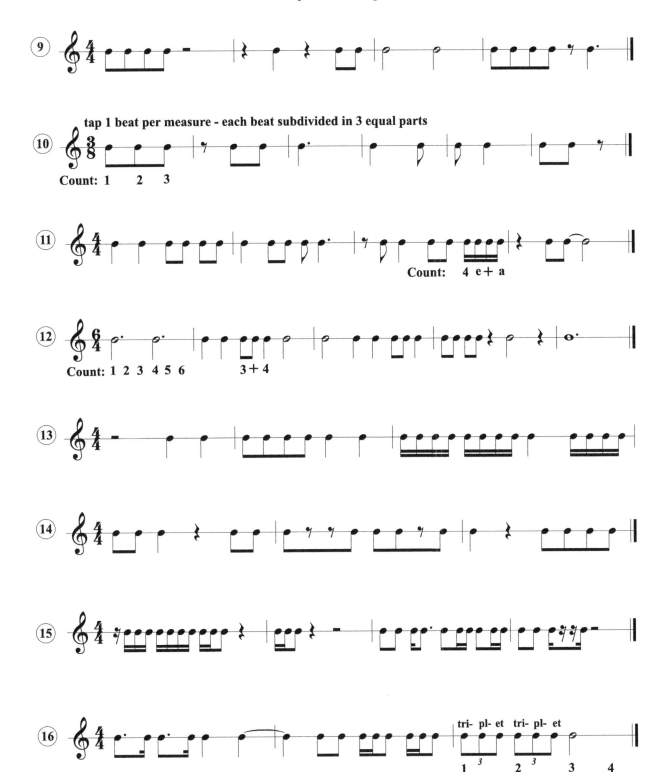

# Lesson 1 ~ The Staff

**Now that you have learned some basic rhythm patterns, it's time to learn about *pitch*.**

- Notes are written on the five lines and four spaces of a *musical staff*. The staff is basically a graph.
- Notes are plotted on the staff and indicate the exact pitches that should be played.
- The *pitch* has to do with the high and low sound vibrations that instruments make.

*The clef* is at the beginning of each staff and indicates the range of the instrument to be used in a piece of music. Guitar music uses the *treble clef*.

*Here are two easy ways to remember the names of the notes placed on the spaces and lines of the staff.*

*Notes in the spaces spell the word "FACE"*      *Remember: FACE rhymes with SPACE*

F            A            C            E

*Notes placed on the lines can be remembered like this:*      *Remember: LINE rhymes with FINE*
*"Every Good Boy Does Fine"*

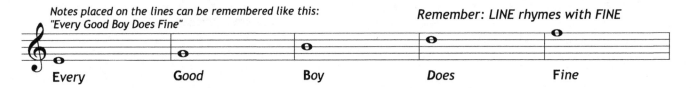

Every       Good       Boy       Does       Fine

### Note Names - the natural notes

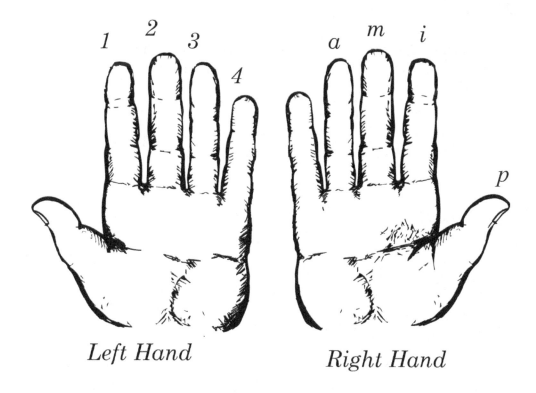

*Left Hand*　　　　*Right Hand*

There are traditional names for the guitarist's fingers.

·　　Numbers are used for the Left Hand or Fretting Hand fingers.

1 = Left Hand index finger
2 = Left Hand middle finger
3 = Left Hand ring finger
4 = Left Hand little (pinkie) finger

The left-hand thumb is typically not used by classical guitarists but fingerstyle guitarists do use it in special circumstances.

·　　Letters are used for the Right Hand or Picking Hand fingers.
　　　The names are abbreviations of the Spanish words for these fingers.

p = pulgar - Right Hand thumb
i = índice - Right Hand index finger
m = médio - Right Hand middle finger
a = anular - Right Hand ring finger

The Right Hand little finger is sometimes used in flamenco guitar playing and for special effects. Often the symbol is "x"

# *Lesson 2* - The Open Strings

*The 6th String is the thickest string and the 1st string is the thinnest.*
*The 6th string has a low pitch and the 1st string has a high pitch.*

## Moving the Bass

## String Crossing with *i* and *m*

## Using *p* with *i* and *m*

# Lesson 3 ~ Notes on the Frets

### F (fa)- First Finger, First Fret, First String

i    m    i          continue i and m alternation

1    p    m    p    m    i

2    m    i    m    i    m  i  m

3    i  m  i

### G (sol) - Third Finger, Third Fret, First String

G is played on the third fret with the third finger.
The note head sits in the first space above the top line on the staff.

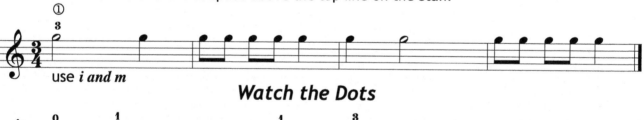

use *i and m*

## Watch the Dots

0    1    1    3

## Opa!

i    m    i    m    i    m    i

Repeat Sign
(go back to the beginning)

## E-F-G in Three

## Flying On the First String

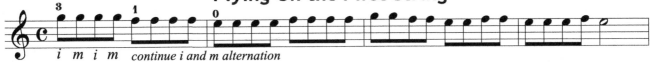

i m i m    continue i and m alternation

## B (ti)- The Open Second String

## Ancient Waltz

Roger Hudson

## C (do)- First Finger, First Fret, Second String

## Land of the Pima

Roger Hudson

### D (re)- Third Finger, Third Fret, Second String

## Big Chicken Dance

*Big Chicken Dance* is a silly song. Have some fun with it!
See if you can sing the words while you play the notes.

R. H.

Big  Chick - en  Dance?  ③  Chick-ens  can't  dance!

chick! - chick! - chick! - chick!  Big  Chick - en  Dance!

## Simple Scale Study

## Siamese Cat Walk

Roger Hudson

## Crossing the Desert

Roger Hudson

## Jumping G's

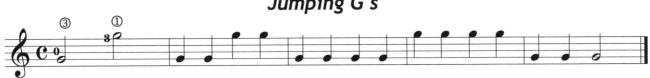

**A (la) - Third String, Second Fret**

## G to G

## Twinkle, Twinkle, Little Star

### Blues Lick

### Four String Combo

Roger Hudson

## Ode to Joy

Ludwig van Beethoven

This is a tie -
let the second note ring but do not pick it

## Igor's Dance

Roger Hudson

hold down left hand fingers 1 and 2 - - - - - - -

## Mystery Castle

Roger Hudson

# Lesson 4 ~ Melody with Bass Accompaniment

*One of the most special features of classical and fingerstyle guitar playing is the use of the right hand thumb (p) to perform a bass accompaniment while the fingers (i, m, and a) play melody and harmony.*

## Opa! (with bass)

## Blues Lick With Bass

## Pentatonic Prelude
Roger Hudson

## Two Middle Aged Elves
Roger Hudson

*12 Bar Blues* is a 12-measure-long musical form that is used in many songs - mostly in jazz, blues, rock, and country music.  "12 Bar Blues Lick" is an example of how this form can be used.

# 12 Bar Blues Lick

Roger Hudson

# Lesson 5 ~ *Block Chords and Arpeggios*

A *chord* is three or more notes played together. Practice the chord below in block form first (notes played exactly at the same time).
1. Plant the right hand fingers on the strings: **p - i - m - a** from the lowest to highest sounding string in the chord.
2. Play the strings together and allow the fingers to follow through freely into the palm of the hand.
3. Make sure the fingers do not collide into the thumb. The thumb (p) follows through toward the floor and the left knee.
4. Do not bounce, twist or jerk the right hand or wrist. Keep the hand steady.

*Arpeggios* are chords whose notes are played one after the other. The right hand position is the same as that for the block chord. Make sure you get good contact with each string before it is played. The timing should be smooth, relaxed and even. There are many arpeggio patterns. For a more in detailed study of arpeggios patterns, refer to *120 Studies for the Right Hand* by Mauro Giuliani.

# The Hidden Passage

Roger Hudson

# Accidentals

## Part 1: sharps #

**READ THIS!**

- *"Accidentals " are notes that do not normally occur in the key (the collection of notes used n a composition).*
- *Composers sometimes use accidentals to take the music in a different and more unpredictable direction.*
- *The piece below entitled "Andante" adds the "sharp" accidentals of G# and C#.*
- *Sharps are indicated by the # sign and mean that the note will be played one fret higher than usual.*
- *The first accidental that appears in the measure will change the other notes of that letter name for the rest of that measure.*

# Andante
*(moderately slow, walking tempo)*

Roger Hudson

# Ballad

Roger Hudson

# The Fig Tree

Roger Hudson

# *Lesson 6* ~ Completing the First Position

## Notes on the 6th String - E, F and G

## Dynamics - *Means changing how loud the music is as you play.*

- *Sometimes the composer has a plan for how loud or soft the music should be.*
- *Some of the common symbols for dynamics are indicated near the notes.*
- *The symbols are abbreviations for Italian words: piano, mezzo-piano, mezzo-forte, forte, fortissimo, and pianissimo.*

# Scary Bass Line

*Suspenseful*

Roger Hudson

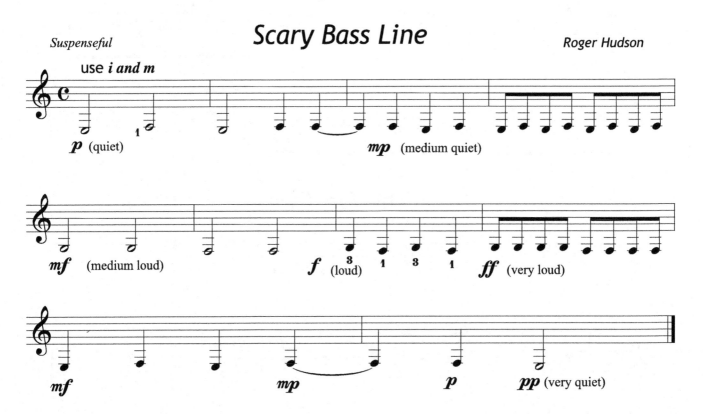

## Notes on the 5th String - A, B, and C

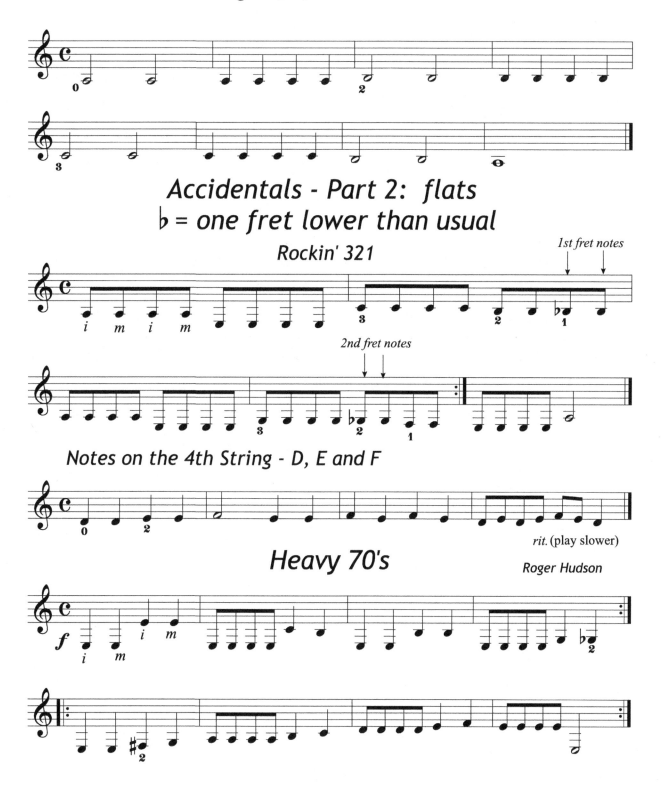

## Accidentals - Part 2:  flats
## ♭ = one fret lower than usual

### Rockin' 321

1st fret notes

2nd fret notes

### Notes on the 4th String - D, E and F

*rit.* (play slower)

## Heavy 70's

Roger Hudson

**Memorization:** *Try to memorize "Asturias".  It is easy if you pay close attention to which measures are repeated and which ones are different.  "Asturias" may look like a lot of notes!  However, there are many repeated patterns.  Measure 1 for example, happens 6 times!*

# Asturias (theme)

Isaac Albeniz

# Lesson 7 ~ *The Key of C Major*

## The C Major Scale

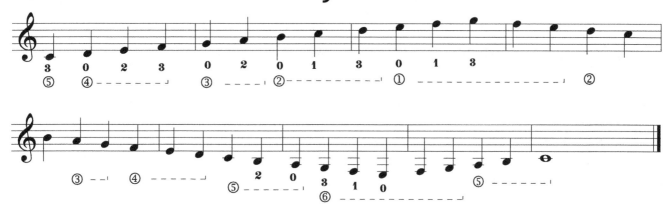

## C Major Scale Study No.1

## C Major Scale Study No.2

# Ode to Joy
## (duet version)

Ludwig van Beethoven
(1770-1827)

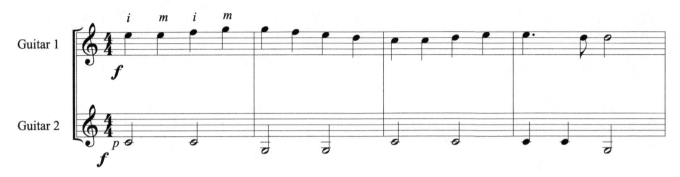

# Song of Victory
## (for Two Guitars)

Roger Hudson

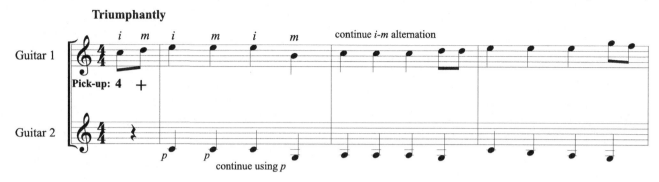

# Arkansas Traveler

Col. Sanford C. Faulkner (1806-1874)

alternate right hand fingers

# Harmony in 6ths

Roger Hudson

# Harmony in 10ths

Roger Hudson

In "The Story of Dorian", the notes of C major are used but D minor is the tonic (main chord). So the piece is actually in the second "mode" of the major key. The second mode is called the "Dorian" mode.

# The Story of Dorian

Roger Hudson

# Four Note Block Chords and Arpeggios

1.  In order to form the block chords in the exercises below, leave left hand fingers down after playing the fretted quarter notes of the arpeggio.
2.  In the last two measures of the exercise there are repeated block chords. Here, the fingers will need to form the notes of the chords quickly and simultaneously.

REMEMBER:  **The notes in the block chord are all played at the same time.**
When two consecutive chords share some of the same notes, the shared note (or notes) should remain fretted when changing from one chord to another.

# Prelude in C

Matteo Carcassi
(1792-1853)

# Counterpoint Study
(holding down bass notes while playing a melody)

Roger Hudson

# Lesson 8 ~ *The Key of A Minor*

*Minor Scales follow a different interval pattern than major scales. Consequently they give a different musical impression. Below are two common types of minor scales in the key of A minor.*

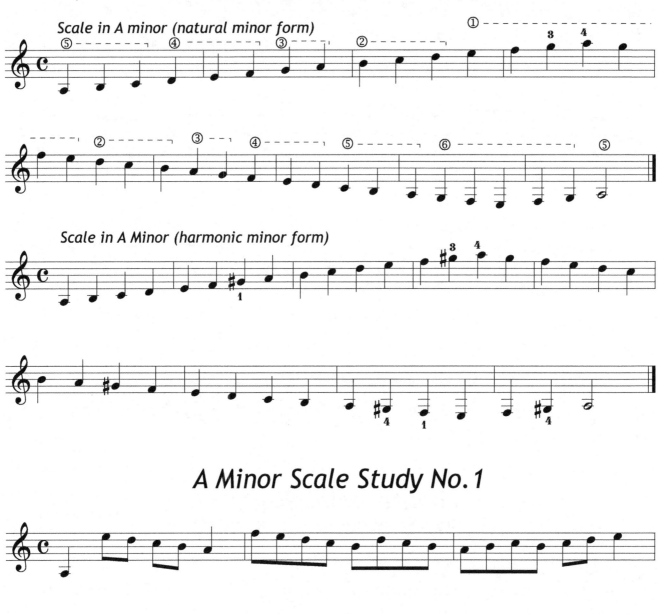

### Scale in A minor (natural minor form)

### Scale in A Minor (harmonic minor form)

## A Minor Scale Study No.1

# A Minor Scale Study No.2

# Korobeiniki

*Russian folksong*

# Malagueña

traditional dance from Málaga, Spain

**Allegro**

**Adagio**

**Allegro**

# Study in A minor

Mauro Giuliani
(1781-1828)

# Españoleta

Old Spanish Dance
Gaspar Sanz (1640-1710)

# Menuett

Johann Krieger
(1651-1735)

*Fine*

*D.C. al Fine*

# Napoleon Crossing the Alps
(for Two Guitars)

*Irish fiddle Tune*
*arr. R. Hudson*

# Chord Symbols and Strummed Chords

*Memorize these 10 basic chord shapes. These will give you a start on learning chords for strumming.*
*- There are many, many, more chords to learn!*
*Instead of showing the actual notes of a chord, **Chord Symbols** - for example E, Am, C, etc. are often used in jazz and popular music to indicate which chord should be played while another musician (or yourself) is singing or playing a melody.*
*- **The shapes must be memorized in order to use them fluently.***

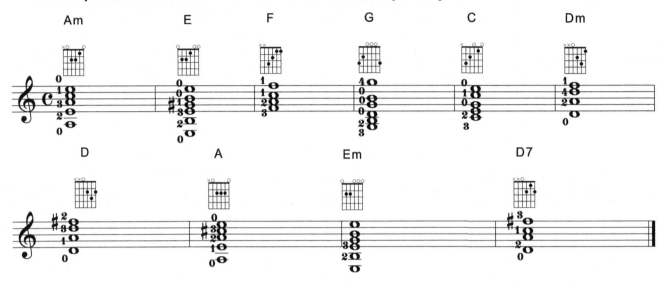

- *"Chord Slash Notation" is often used to indicate the rhythm pattterns for strummed chords.*
- *Down-stroke and up-stroke symbols indicate the direction of the strum.*
- *Chord Symbols indicate the chords to be played.*
- *Chords may be strummed in a variety of ways - using i, p or with a pick (plectrum).*

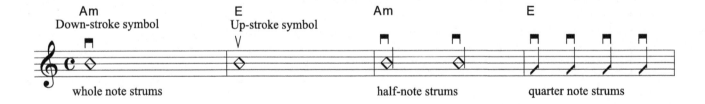

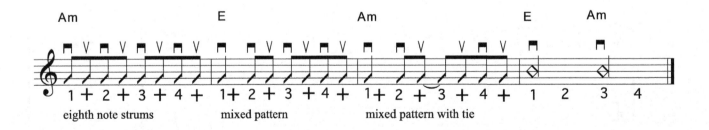

# Surfing Spanish Style

*Take turns playing the Guitar 1 and 2 parts with your duet partner*

Roger Hudson

*Surf Rock Feel*

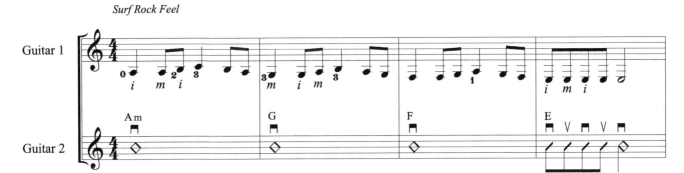

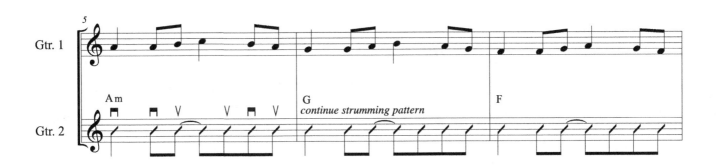

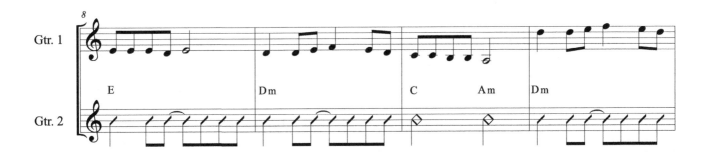

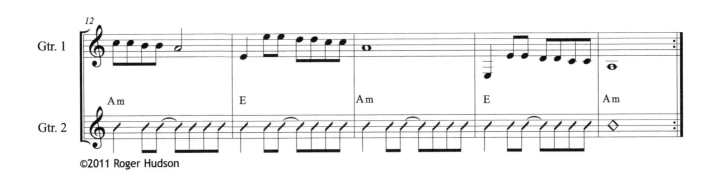

# Lesson 9 ~ *The Key of G Major*

With the introduction of G major we find the use of a **key signature** indicating an accidental that will be frequently used. In the case of G major, an F# is needed to make the scale sound like a major scale. Instead of putting a sharp sign before every F, the sharp sign is positioned after every clef on the top line of the staff. This means **all** F notes will be played as F#.

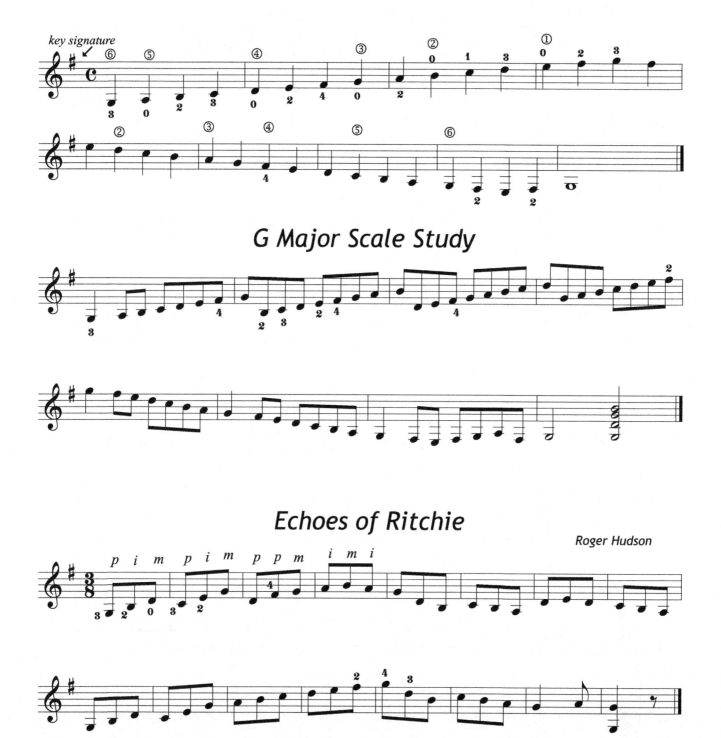

## G Major Scale Study

## Echoes of Ritchie

Roger Hudson

# Cripple Creek
## *for guitar duet*

Appalachian Folksong
arranged by R. Hudson

# Prelude
Opus 59

Matteo Carcassi
(1797-1853)

*use either right hand pattern*

# Picking with Travis

Roger Hudson

# Andantino

Ferdinando Carulli
(1770-1841)

# Tremolo Study

Roger Hudson

**Largo** ♩ = 50

*continue right hand pattern - play evenly*

# Lesson 10 ~ The Key of E Minor

*Scale in E Minor (natural minor form)*

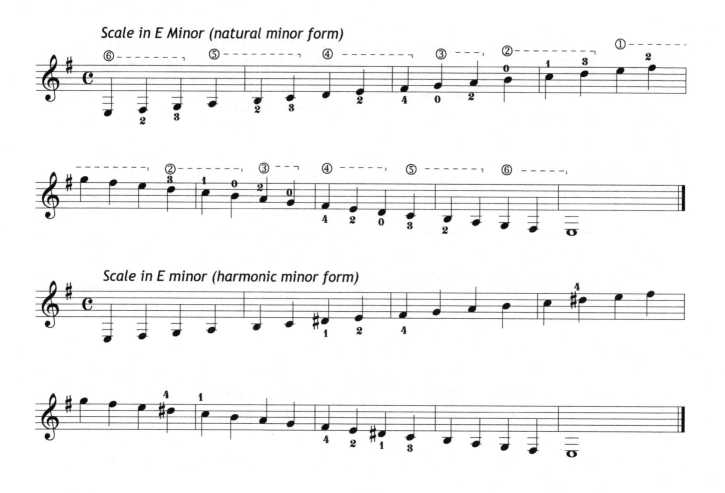

*Scale in E minor (harmonic minor form)*

## E Minor Scale Study

alternate right hand fingers

# Interlude in E Minor

Roger Hudson

# Waltz in E Minor

Ferdinando Carulli
(1770-1841)

## Arpeggio Speed Study

# The Banks of Newfoundland

Moderato

19th Century Sea Chantey
arr. Roger Hudson

# Moving up the Fingerboard

**B** - *1st string, 7th fret*     **C** - *1st string, 8th fret*     **D** - *1st string, 10th fret*     **E** - *1st string, 12th fret*

### READ THIS!
- *When performing higher and lower first string notes together, the lower note will need to be played on a string other than the first string.*
- *In "Swamp Daze" the the high G will be played on the 2nd string, 8th fret, because the high B (a higher note than G) is played on the first string.*
- *Can you figure out some other places on the fingerboard where the G and B could be played together? Refer to the chart on page 4 for help.*

REMEMBER: *The circled number is the string number.*

## Swamp Daze

Roger Hudson

# The Melodic Minor and Jazz Minor Scales

In addition to the natural and harmonic minor scales, there is another minor scale - the Melodic Minor Scale. In this scale the 6th and 7th notes of the scale are raised 1/2 step (one fret) **only** when the scale is ascending. When the scale is descending, the 6th and 7th notes return to the natural minor form. Listen closely to the effect that is produced by the raising and lowering of the 6th and 7th notes (also called "scale degrees"). J. S. Bach's "Bourée" on page 52 is a brilliant example of the melodic minor scale in a composition.

### Scale in E Minor (melodic minor form)

*Jazz Minor is the same pattern as the ascending melodic minor scale but does not go back to natural when descending.*

### Scale in E Minor (jazz minor form)

## Harmonic Minor in 7th position

*Playing notes higher up on the fretboard is not difficult if you can stay in a fixed position.*

- On the guitar, a **position** is determined by where the left hand 1st finger will fret the notes in a musical phrase.

- The other left hand fingers will fall in line after the 1st finger. In the example below, the **1st finger notes will play on the 7th fret. 2nd finger = 8th fret, 3rd finger = 9th fret, 4th finger = 10th fret**

*Learning this partial E minor harmonic minor scale in 7th position will allow the Guitar 1 part of "Katibim" (page 54) to be easily learned . The Guitar 1 part uses **only** these notes!*

51

# Bourée
## (duet version)

Johann Sebastian Bach
(1685-1750)
arr. by Roger Hudson

Guitar 1
Guitar 2

Gtr. 1
Gtr. 2

Gtr. 1
Gtr. 2

Bourée

*The original version of this piece is played as a solo and is the 5th Movement of Bach's Lute Suite in E Minor (BWV 996).
You can actually try this version as a solo by playing both parts at the same time.*

*However, you will need to change many of the fingerings!*

# Katibim

(duet version)

*Turkish Folk Song*
*arr. R. Hudson*

# Lesson 11 ~ *The Key of D Major*

## The D Major Scale

*2nd position*  The D Major Scale may also be played entirely in 2nd position.

## D Major Scale Study

## Ascending and Descending Slurs

*Playing ascending slurs - **1.** Start with the 1st finger down  **2.** Pick the string **3.** Firmly "hammer" the 2nd finger down without picking the string again  \* Do not lift up the 1st finger*

*Playing descending slurs - **1.** Position both the 1st and 2nd fingers on the fingerboard  **2.** Pick the string **3.** "Pull" or flick the 2nd finger off the string and toward the floor.  \* Do not lift up the 1st finger until the open string is played.*

*Ascending Slur (hammer-on)*              *Descending Slur (pull-off)*

# Renaissance Faire

Roger Hudson

## Rhythmic Syncopation

*Ties are often used to make rhythms a little less predictable. In the example below a tie is used between the "and" or upbeat of beat 2 and the down beat of 3. This means that there will not be a note played on beat 3. Two tied notes ring as a single note.*

# Goodnight Prince
### (Lullaby for Elijah)

Roger Hudson

*Slowly and Majestically*

# Barring 2 or 3 Strings

As we saw earlier with the common F chord, it is sometimes necessary to hold down two or more strings with the 1st finger. This is called a "bar" or "barre". Bars often require a lot of practice, so keep trying! The exercise below only uses a bar for 2 or 3 strings. This will help you to prepare for barring 4,5 and 6 strings later.

- The chords below will be used on the Guitar 2 part of "Jazzy Weather" on page 59.
- Roman numerals( **I, II, IV** etc.) are used to indicate the fret number where the bar will be placed.
- The Arabic numeral (**2, 3, 4,** or **5**) indicates how many strings will be barred
- A Roman numeral alone indicates a *full bar* (all 6 strings).

## D major Scale in 7th Position (One Octave)

The Guitar 1 Part of "Jazzy Weather" (page 59) will be played in the 7th position to allow higher melody notes to be used.

**Position Shifting** - Sometimes it is not possible or efficient to stay in one position. A "position shift" may be needed to complete a musical phrase. This must be done smoothly. The shift should be seamless.

Practice the excerpt below from J.S. Bach's famous "Minuet" to get familiar with shifting positions.

## Minuet

J. S. Bach

# Jazzy Weather
## (duet version)

Roger Hudson

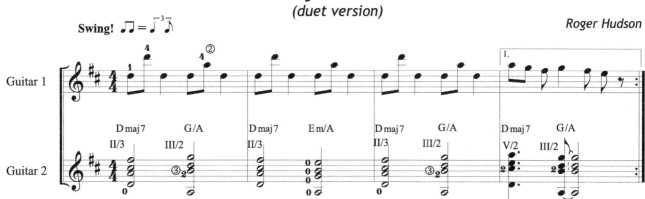

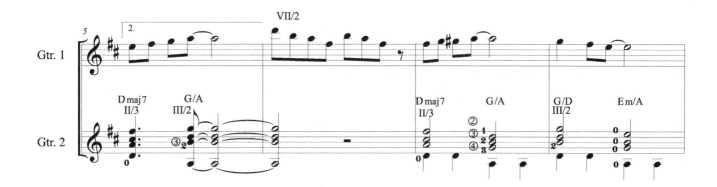

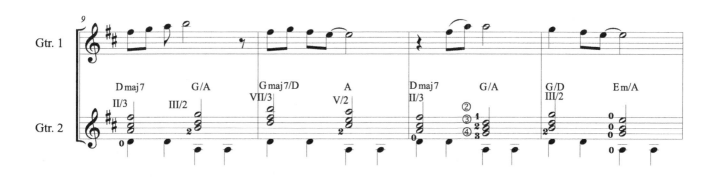

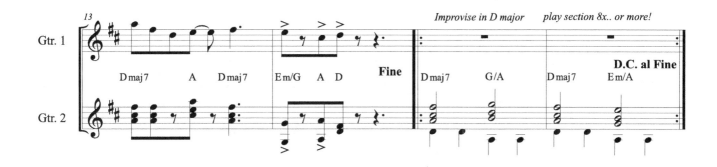

# Lesson 12 ~ *The Key of B minor*

### Scale in B Minor (natural minor form)

### Scale in B Minor (natural minor form) - 2nd Position

### Scale in B Minor (harmonic minor form)

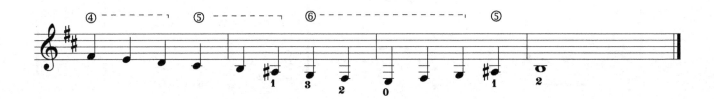

# B Minor Scale Study

## Barring 4, 5 or 6 Strings

As you begin to play in keys containing more and more accidentals, barring strings becomes more common.  Here are some basic tips for playing bar chords.

1.  Keep the 1st finger (barring finger) as flat as possible, close to the fret but not directly on it.
2.  Make sure the guitar neck is in a good playing position (about 30-45 degrees from the floor).
3.  Keep the left arm as relaxed as possible with the elbow down, close to your body.
4.  Keep the left thumb in the center of the back of the guitar neck without digging into it.
5.  Contact with the neck should be with the pad of the left thumb - not the tip.

# Study in B Minor

*opus 35, no.22*

Fernando Sor
(1778-1839)

# Moon Tide

Roger Hudson

# Lesson 13 ~ The Key of A Major

### The A Major Scale

### A Major Scale Study

### A Major Chord Study

# Prelude

Opus 59

Matteo Carcassi
(1797-1853)

# Frankie

American Folk Song

# Um Puoco de Bossa

## (A Little Bit of Bossa)

Roger Hudson

# Lesson 14 ~ The Key of F# Minor

*Scale in F# Minor (natural minor form)*

*Scale in F# Minor (harmonic minor form)*

## Warm-up in F# Minor

# More Position Shifting

It is important to remember that string instruments - including the guitar - can play the same musical phrases in more than one location on the instrument. This allows string players to get a variety of tone colors. The effect can be similar to the difference between two orchestral instruments playing exactly the same notes - clarinet vs. flute for instance. In order to achieve this *timbral* (tone color) contrast, guitarists should become familiar with the entire fingerboard. Acquiring skill at changing positions can build a guitarist's confidence - a necessary trait for a successful performer.

In the examples below, an ancient melody known as *Leoni* is used to practice moving from one position to another.
At rehearsal letters A nd B, the melody is the same but in different positions. At rehearsal letter C the melody is an octave higher.

69

# Beguine in Beijing

duet

Roger Hudson

70

# Mixed Emotions

Roger Hudson

# Lesson 15 ~ The Key of E Major

## The E Major Scale

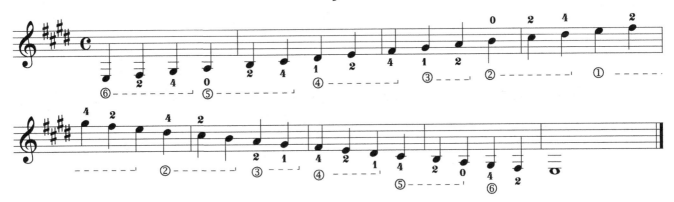

## E Major Scale Study No.1

## E Major Speed Study

# Prelude

Roger Hudson

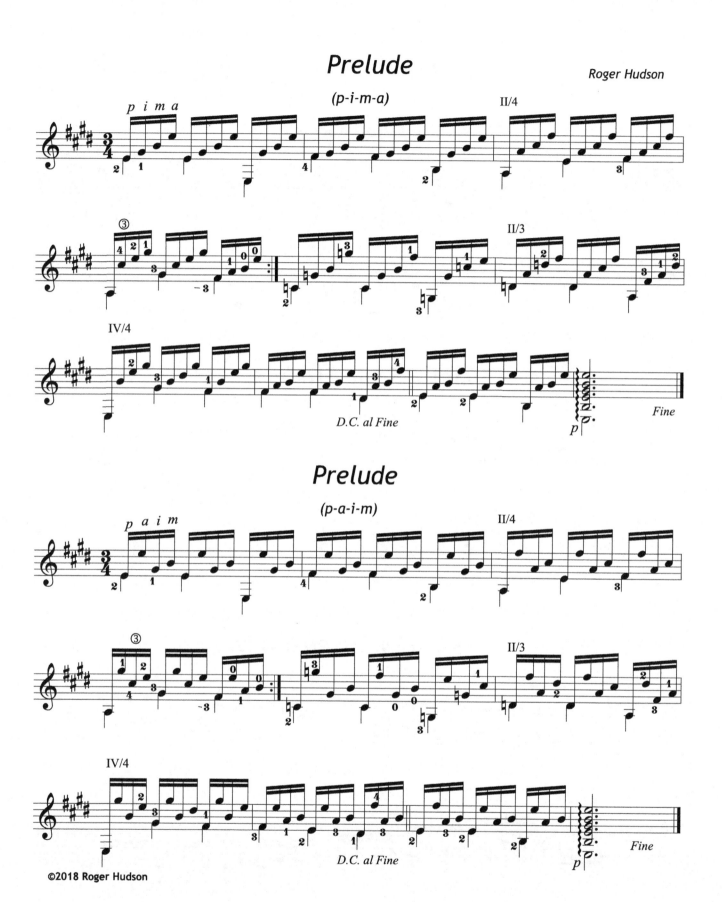

# Waiting for a Friend

Roger Hudson

# Softly and Tenderly

Will L. Thompson
(1847-1909)
arranged by Roger Hudson

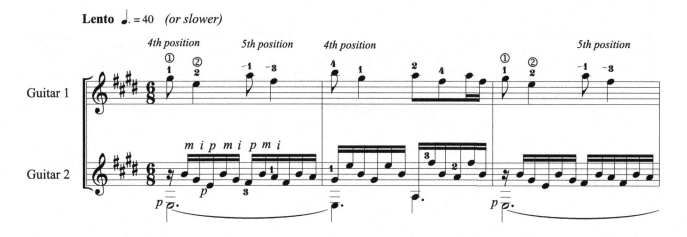

Softly and Tenderly

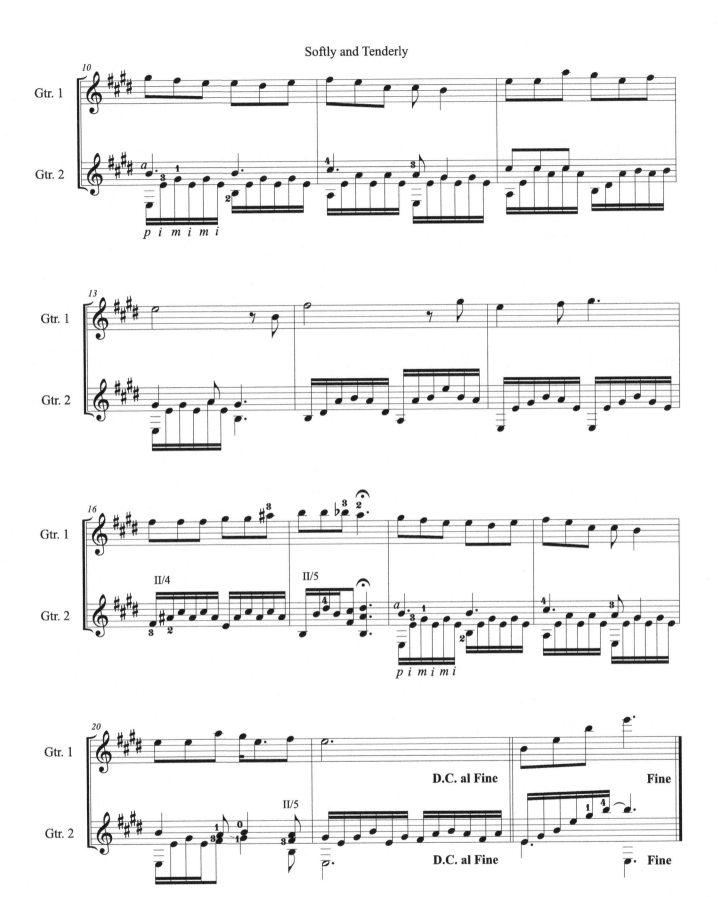

# Got Rhythm?

Roger Hudson

78

# Lesson 16 ~ The Key of C# Minor

*Scale in C# minor (natural minor form)*

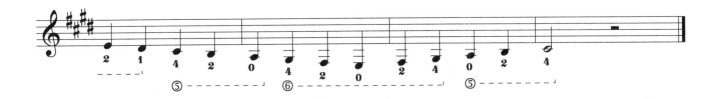

*Scale in C# minor (harmonic minor form)*

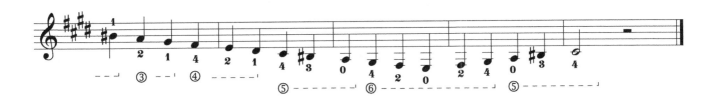

## C# Minor Scale Study

**Practice these chord shapes before learning the *Study in C# Minor***

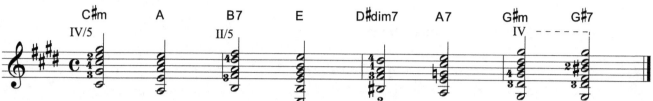

## Study in C# Minor
### (arpeggios, 5 and 6 string bar chords)

R. H.

# Movable Scales

- Scale patterns which use fretted notes only and no open strings are considered *movable*.
- The movable scale's left hand *finger pattern* used in one key may be transferred to a new key.
- The letter name of the key changes depending upon where the root (starting note of the scale) is located.
- In the example below, a C# minor scale (natural form) is played in 4th position with no open strings. If this entire pattern were moved to the 5th position, the scale would be D minor.
- It is very important to **memorize the patterns of movable scales!** They are very practical for learning musical phrases and for improvising.

### C# Minor Scale - 4th Position

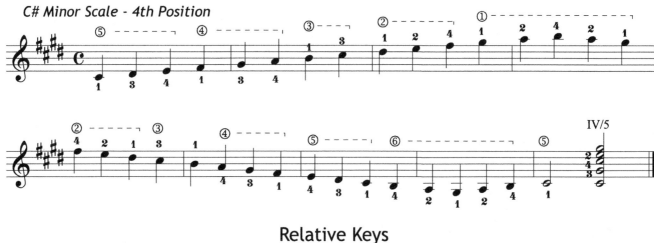

## Relative Keys

C# minor shares the same key signature as E major. By starting the same pattern, on but on E (4th finger), an E major scale is produced.

### E Major Scale - 4th Position

## The "jazz" chords below will be used to play "Winding Down" on page 82.

---

81

# Winding Down

Roger Hudson

**Easy Going**

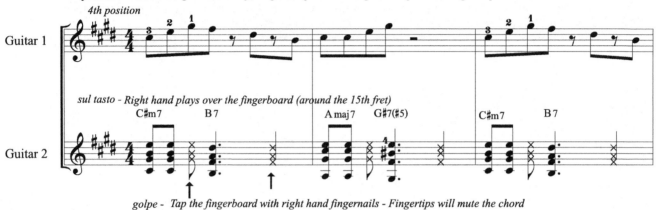

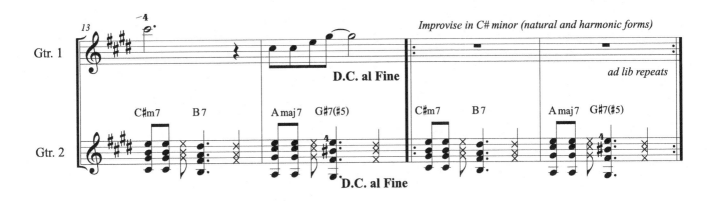

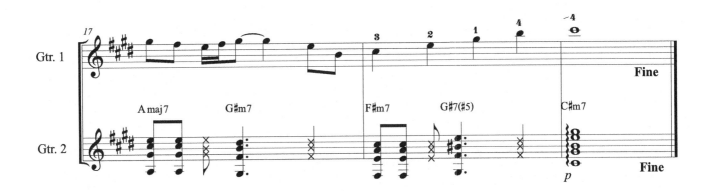

# Lesson 17 ~ The Key of F Major

### The F Major Scale

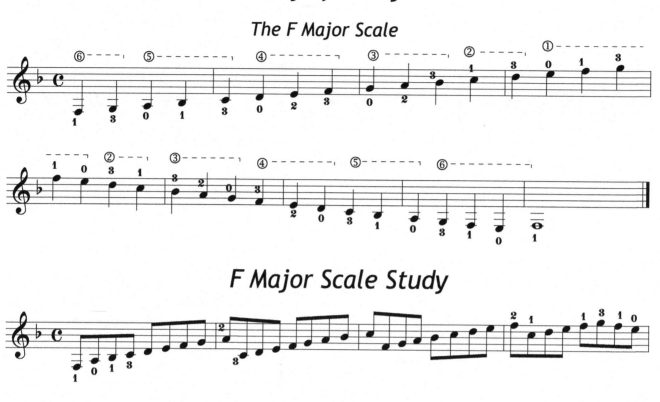

## F Major Scale Study

Based on the finger pattern we learned from C#minor and E major in Lesson 16, playing and memorizing an F major scale is the same pattern transferred to 5th position.

### F Major Scale - 5th Position

# Chord Formation and Major Scale Harmonization

- The same notes in a key that are used for scales are also used for the chords in that key.
- The simplest chords are called **triads**. Triads are a combination of 3 different notes.
- Triads are formed by taking a starting note, called the *root* note and adding notes a 3rd and 5th higher than the root.

An F major chord uses F - A - C. Any chordal combination (block chord, strummed chord, or arpeggio) of F-A-C is an F Major chord. *Doubling* (more than one of the same letter in the chord) may also occur.

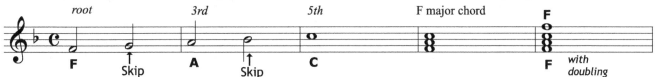

To *harmonize* a scale - building chords - first start with the notes of the scale...

...then add a 3rd and 5th to every note of the scale.
- The *intervals*, or distances between the root, 3rd and 5th of a chord determine whether that chord will be major, minor, diminished or augmented.
- To understand this more fully, concentrated study of Music Theory is essential. That requires a different book! The chord symbol for major is the letter only (F, C, etc.), minor uses "m" after the letter (Am, Dm etc.), and diminished chords usually use the abbreviation "dim". Augmented (aug) triads are not formed from major scales.

- The *voicing*, or arrangement of the notes in the triad, along with doublings, may be varied.
- Shown below are some common voicings of chords in F major.

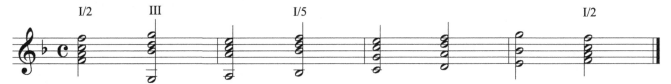

- When the bass note of a chord is other than the root note, the chord is called an *inversion*.
- Chord symbols with inversions will show the name of the chord first and then the alternate bass note.

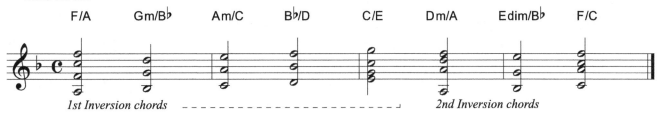

# Floating Dream

sostenuto (sustained - allow notes to freely ring into one another)

Roger Hudson

# More Slur Practice

In order to articulate musical phrases in various ways, learning and practicing slurs in all finger combinations is crucial for developing strong left hand technique. We will use the 5th position F major scale to practice some of these combinations in a melodic setting.

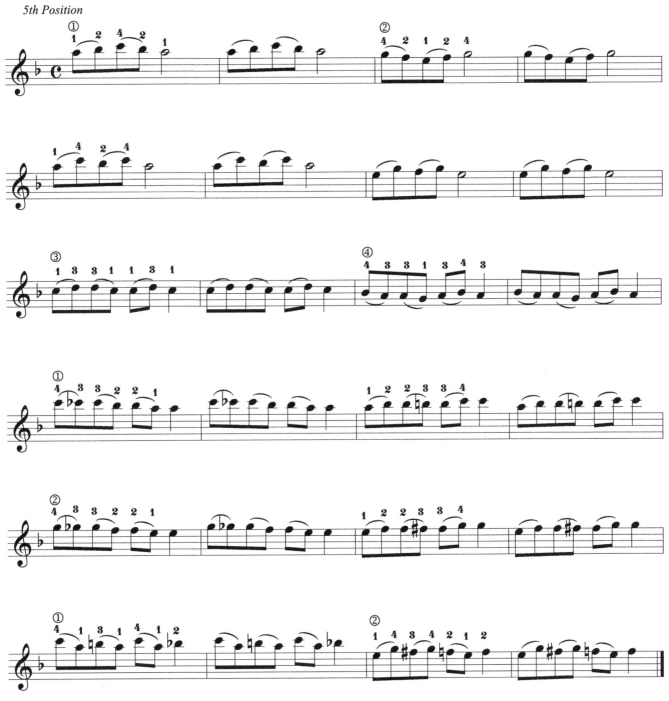

# Romantic Prelude

(duet)

Roger Hudson

Romantic Prelude

Romantic Prelude

Romantic Prelude

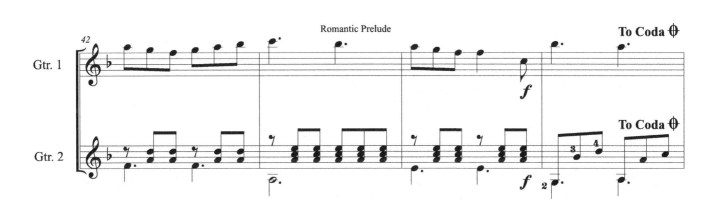

# Lesson 18 ~ The Key of D Minor

*Scale in D minor (natural minor form)*

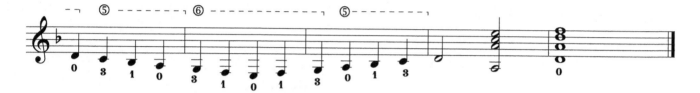

*Scale in D Minor (harmonic minor form)*

*Scale in D Minor (natural minor form) - 5th Position*

**D minor uses the same 5th position finger pattern as F major but begins with the 1st finger on the 5th string**

## Position Shifting Between Scale Patterns

Moving from a first (open) position scale to a movable scale may be required for a musical passage.
Practice the exercise below to gain smoothness in shifting between 1st and 5th position scales.

## Complex Time Signatures

To add some rhythmic variety to a composition, some composers will use time signatures which are less common. In certain cultures, notably in Eastern Europe, Asia and the Middle East, complex time signatures are regularly used and have been for centuries. These time signatures are sometimes known as *asymmetric* because they have unevenly stressed beats. Complex time signatures typically use 5, 7, 9 and 11. These numbers are usually subdivided into uneven groups: 4+3=7, 5+4=9, 6+5=11 etc. "Khorumi" uses a 3+2=5 pattern.

### *Khorumi*

Folk Dance from Republic of Georgia
adaptation by Roger Hudson

# Drop D Tuning

One of the guitar's special features is the capability of changing the tuning of the instrument. This allows the player access to notes that would not be available in standard tuning. These non-standard tunings are called *altered tunings*. Altered tunings may also allow the guitarist to perform familiar finger patterns and movements while achieving a different musical effect with those patterns and movements. One of the most basic altered tunings is called *dropped-D tuning* or simply *drop-D tuning*.
It is made by tuning the 6th string down to D while leaving the remaining strings in standard tuning.

*REMEMBER: When using Drop-D tuning, notes that are played on the 6th string must be played two frets higher than normal because of the lowered 6th string.*

## The Coventry Carol

16th Century England
arranged by Roger Hudson

play at 5th fret

play at 5th fret

# Lesson 19 ~ *The Key of B♭ Major*

## The B♭ Major Scale

## Study in B♭ Major

R. H.

# Sweet Surprise

Roger Hudson

*plant p on 5th string here*

# Lesson 20 ~ The Key of G Minor

*Scale in G minor (natural minor form)*

*Scale in G Minor (harmonic minor form)*

## G Minor Scale Study

R. H.

*Scale in G Minor (natural minor form) -  2nd Position - 4th String root*

*Scale in G Minor (melodic minor form) -  2nd Position - 4th String root*

*Scale in G Minor (natural minor form) -  5th Position - 4th String root*

# Mazurka

("Tra Veglia e Sonno")

P. Forte and L. Canora
*arrangement by R. Hudson*

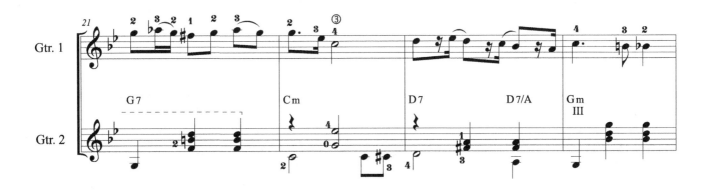

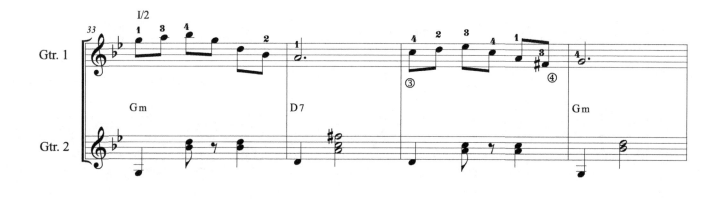

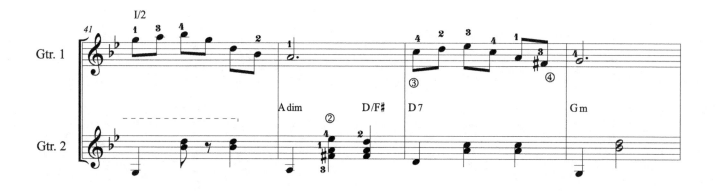

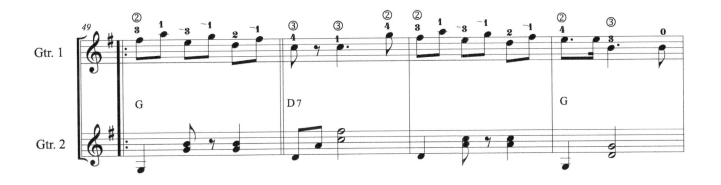

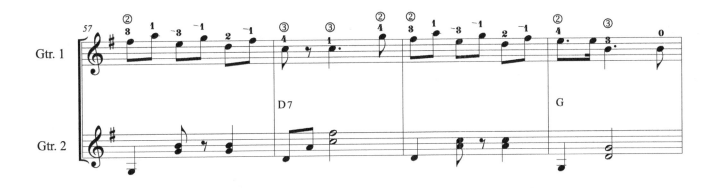

# Labyrinth

Roger Hudson

# Complete Chart of Key Signatures with Major Keys - Relative Minor Keys - Modes

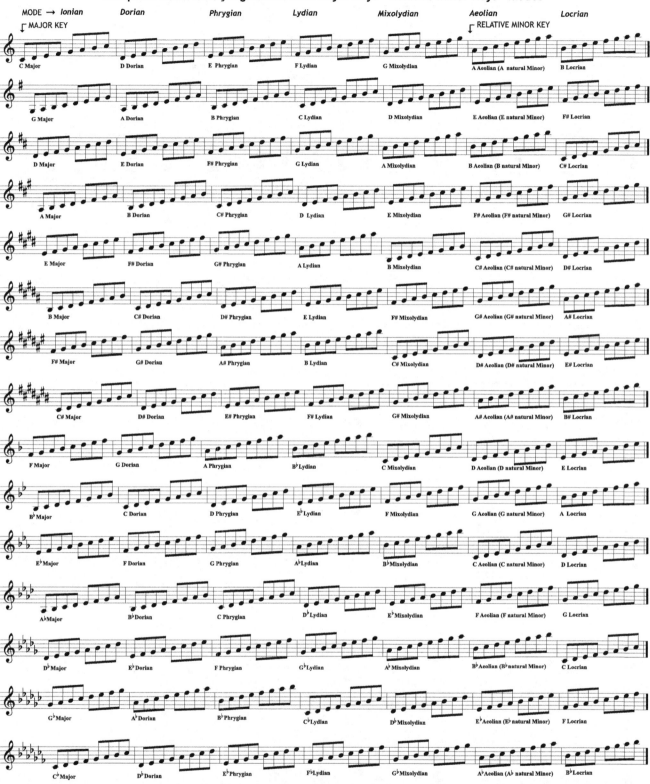

ADDITIONAL REPERTOIRE

107

# Rainy Scene

*Reflectively*

Roger Hudson

# Kelly's Green Jig

Roger Hudson

# Greensleeves

16th Century England

# Daydream

Roger Hudson

# Simple Gifts

Shaker Hymn (1848)
Joseph Brackett, Jr.
(1797-1882)
arr. R. Hudson

# Fandango

Roger Hudson

# Interlude

*Study in 3rds, 6ths and 10ths*

Roger Hudson

# Canon

Johann Pachelbel
(1653-1706)
arr. R.Hudson

Canon

# Flamenco Fantasy
### for 2 Guitars

Roger Hudson

## Flamenco Fantasy

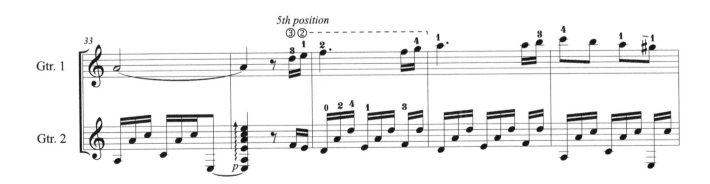

# Flamenco Fantasy

# Silent Night

Franz Gruber
arr. Roger Hudson

# Jesu, Joy of Man's Desiring

Johann Sebastian Bach
(1685-1750)
arr. Roger Hudson

# Harp Strings

Roger Hudson

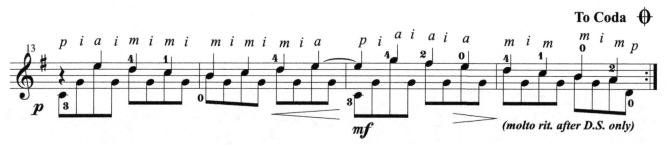

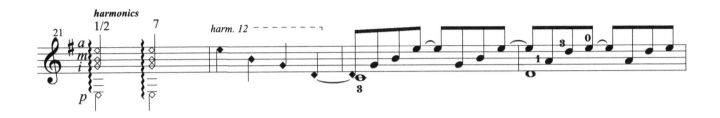

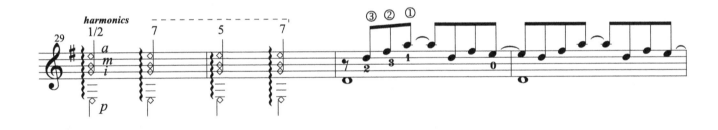

**D.S. al Coda**

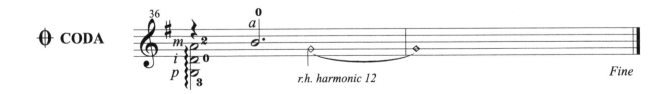

*Fine*

# Gymnopedie no. 1

Erik Satie (1866-1925)
arr. Roger Hudson

⑥ = D (re)

Lent et douloureux

# Blue Stairways

Roger Hudson

# Sambavacation

Roger Hudson